BAZOOKA BOYS!

Be Strong & Be Brave...
for the Lord your God is with you.

Deuteronomy 31:6

By
Kristie Kerr & Paula Yarnes
with
Jeff Kerr & Aaron Broberg

Unless otherwise indicated, all Scripture quotations are taken from the Holy Bible, New Living Translation, copyright ©1996, 2004, 2007 by Tyndale House Foundation. Used by permission of Tyndale House Publishers, Inc., Carol Stream, Illinois 60188. All rights reserved.

THE HOLY BIBLE, NEW INTERNATIONAL VERSION®, NIV® Copyright © 1973, 1978, 1984, 2011 by Biblica, Inc.™ Used by permission. All rights reserved worldwide.

Scripture taken from The Message. Copyright ©1993, 1994, 1995, 1996, 2000, 2001, 2002. Used by permission of NavPress Publishing Group.

Scripture taken from the Contemporary English Version ©1991, 1992, 1995 by American Bible Society, Used by Permission.

Scripture taken from the Common English Bible P.O. Box 801 201 Eighth Avenue South Nashville, TN 37202-0801

Scripture taken from the International Standard Version Release 2.1. Copyright ©1996–2012 the ISV Foundation. All rights reserved internationally.

ISBN: 987-0-9840312-8-3

Printed in the United States of America

1st Printing

CONTENTS

Dedicated to the boys who inspire us:

To Charlie whose tender heart and quiet spirit
remind us that **STRENGTH ISN'T ALWAYS LOUD**.

To Hunter who is **TENACIOUS AND KIND**...
and came up with the name Bazooka Boys.

To Chase who **LOVES UNCONDITIONALLY**.

To Reed who lit his homework on fire...
and then became an **HONOR STUDENT**.

To Jacob, the boy with the sensitive heart,
that captures people with his **LOVE FOR JUSTICE AND ALL THINGS SILLY**.

To Levi whose **DETERMINATION COULD DEMOLISH MOUNTAINS**
& smile could melt away the debris

To Zach who is a **TRUSTWORTHY, CONFIDENT, KIND-HEARTED** young man,
and NEVER forgets to kiss his mom goodnight!

To Li who is **KIND AND LOVING** and ALWAYS follows the rules!

To Stewart. The **TWINKLE IN YOUR EYE** and the tenderness in your heart
remind us that God really does make dreams come true.

You amaze us.
Go change the world.

Bazooka Boys ★ Knowing God

GETTING TO KNOW HIM

WHAT'S THE POINT?
GOD KNOWS EVERYTHING ABOUT YOU,
AND HE WANTS YOU TO KNOW EVERYTHING ABOUT HIM.

THEME VERSE:

The Lord is close to all who call on Him.
Psalm 145:18

RELATED BIBLE PASSAGE:

Exodus 4:1–17

Caleb was six years old when he met Jacob. It had been raining for a few days, and the baseball fields by his house had flooded and turned into one giant mud pit. Caleb stood along the side of the field, wondering if he should jump in. Suddenly, he saw Jacob standing on the other side of the field, sizing up the situation. They caught each others eye, gave each other a nod, and both jumped headfirst into the gooey black mud.

They've been best friends ever since.

Having a good friend is a super cool thing. You can ride your bikes together, play catch, and hang out playing your favorite video game. A good friend is someone you know you can count on, someone who has your back and will always stand beside you. It's cool to know that there is someone you know will be there for you.

And you know what? God wants to be a friend like that.

Sometimes it can seem like God is great big and far away. It can feel like He is just way too big to care about you. But the truth is, God wants to be your friend!

Isn't that crazy? The great big God who made the entire universe wants to be friends with you.

Bazooka Boys ★ Knowing God

Psalm 25:10 says, *"O Lord, You are the friend of Your worshippers . . ."* (CEV).

God already knows everything about you. He knows what you're thinking, what you're feeling, what you're going to do today, and even what you're going to do tomorrow! The Bible tells us He even knows how many hairs you have on your head!

I Peter 1:2 says, *"God the Father knew you and chose you long ago."* Not only does He know everything about you, but He **CHOSE** you to be His friend! Imagine the coolest, strongest, smartest, most amazing person in the world deciding that, out of all the people in the entire universe, He wants to be friends with you. That's pretty amazing!

"...BUT THE PEOPLE WHO KNOW THEIR GOD WILL BE STRONG AND TAKE ACTION."
—DANIEL 11:32

God knows you. God loves you. And God wants you to know Him too.

So, how do you get to know God better? The same way Caleb got to know Jacob better—by spending time with him. And the more time Caleb spent with Jacob, the more he discovered the things that were important to him.

It's the same way with God.

GOD KNOWS EVERYTHING ABOUT YOU, AND HE WANTS YOU TO KNOW EVERYTHING ABOUT HIM.

There are three ways we can get to know God better.

 **1. READING THE BIBLE**

The Bible is a letter from God to you! God has lots of things that He wants to say to you. He wants to tell you about Himself. He wants to tell you about things He has done for other people. He wants to give you instructions for living your life in a way that will make Him happy.

So He gave us the Bible. He told some people, many years ago, to write down some very powerful stories and words that would help you and me understand Him better. Now, you and I can read the Bible and learn what God is like!

You can read the stories and see how God helped people. You can see how He told them to live. You can learn about His heart and how He thinks and most importantly, how much He loves you.

Travis was facing something difficult and he didn't know what to do. He had to get up in front of his whole class to give a book report. He was scared to death of talking in front of people. His knees would shake and his hands would get sweaty and he'd feel like he was going to puke. What was he going to do?

One day he opened his Bible and found a story about a man named Moses. God asked Moses to lead His people out of a really bad situation. He was to go before the Pharoah, who was the King of Egypt, and tell him to free God's people from slavery. Moses was scared! He did not want to

Bazooka Boys ★ Knowing God

stand in front of the King. I can imagine that his knees were shaking and his hands were sweaty and he wanted to puke—just like Travis.

But here's what God said to Moses: *"When you speak, I will be with you and give you the words to say"* (Exodus 4:12, CEV).

Whoa! That's exactly what Travis needed to hear. It was so cool that the words God had said to Moses in the Bible could be so helpful to Travis now. He wrote the words on a little card and carried it with him on the days before he had to give his speech. When the day finally came, he read the card one more time, took a deep breath, and got up in front of the class confident that God was with him and would help him do his very best.

The Bible is full of stories just like this one that can help us get through the tough things we face in our lives. It has all kinds of wisdom and special help for us.

God uses the Bible to speak to us, but it also tells us what God is like. We learn that He is strong and He will protect us. Proverbs 18:10 says, *"The name of the Lord is a strong fortress; the godly run to him and are safe."* We can know, by reading the Bible, that God is not only powerful, but that He will protect us.

"I HAVE HIDDEN YOUR WORD IN MY HEART, THAT I MIGHT NOT SIN AGAINST YOU."
—PSALM 119:11

We learn that God is perfect. He never makes mistakes. He never changes. We can know that He will love us the same today as He did yesterday and will love us just as much tomorrow.

The Bible is God's adventure map for you. It's important that you read it every day so that you can learn more and more what God is like and what He wants you to do.

The second way we can know God better is by:

 **2. TALKING TO GOD**

When Caleb and Jacob were walking home from their mud pit adventure, they couldn't stop talking about how awesome it was. Caleb said, "That was so cool when you slid through the mud into home plate!" Jacob replied, "Oh yeah . . . or when you tackled me that one time? I can't believe how muddy we are!" They went back and forth, recounting their awesome day while the mud dripped off their shirts and shoes.

Not only did they have fun acting like crazy people in the mud, but every time they remembered what they had done and talked about it, they became closer friends. With every new adventure they had came new stories and new memories that bound them together as best buds.

> "ASK ME, AND I WILL TELL YOU REMARKABLE SECRETS . . ."
>
> —JEREMIAH 33:3

God wants us to talk to Him just like we talk to our friends. Actually, praying to God is really just talking to Him. He wants you to talk to Him about the things that are bothering you, the things you're excited about, and the things you're thankful for. He loves it when you share your life with Him.

Something cool happens when you talk to God. You'll begin to feel closer to Him just like you do when you are talking to your friends! It's so awesome to know He cares about the things you care about. He is always listening, and He's the best friend you could ever have.

Not only can you talk to God, He will talk to you too! Jeremiah 33:3 says, *"Ask me, and I will tell you remarkable secrets . . ."*. You may not hear His voice out loud like you hear your mom or dad, but God will speak to your heart. I always try to write down (or even draw a picture of) the words I feel God is speaking to me so I can remember what He is saying to me. And when God speaks to you, it will always line up with what the Bible says.

If you will listen, God will speak to you. He'll give you answers to your problems. He'll challenge you to improve your attitude or behavior. He'll make you feel better when you're sad or frustrated. He'll talk to you about your future.

When God appeared to Moses and told him to lead his people out of slavery, I'm sure Moses was totally freaked out. But I think it's pretty cool that God talked to Moses. He not only gave Moses direction and instructions, but He said things to Moses that gave him courage even though he was afraid.

God is talking to you all the time. Now, it may not be in a voice you can hear, but God will speak to you. When I hear God talking to me, its like I hear the words inside my head, and I know they aren't my own thoughts. You can talk to God, and He will talk to you too!

And the last way we can grow closer to God is to:

 ## 3. GO TO CHURCH

Have you ever been on a team or in a club? It's pretty cool to spend time with kids who are interested in the same things you are. You can learn from each other, help each other get better at the stuff you care about, and support each other when you go through hard times.

Church is a place where you can discover more about God and spend time with people who love Him just like you do. You'll hear stories about the things He's done in the past. You'll learn about what's in the Bible, what makes God happy, and what He doesn't want you to do. And you'll make lots of great friends and have a lot of fun too!

It's important to read your Bible and talk to God when you are at home, but something really amazing happens when you hang out with other people who believe in God like you do. It helps you grow stronger in your faith. You can talk to your teachers and your friends about God. You can ask questions about the things you're unsure about. You can have people pray for you and your family.

Make sure that you come to church often. It's important to spend time with other people who believe in God like you do!

GOD KNOWS EVERYTHING ABOUT YOU, AND HE WANTS YOU TO KNOW EVERYTHING ABOUT HIM.

Closing Prayer: Dear God, thank You that You know me. Thank You that you want to be my friend and that you have lots of adventures planned for my life. I want to know more about you too. Help me to spend time reading the Bible, talking to You, and learning more about You at church. Thank You for choosing me to be your friend. Amen.

DOODLE PAGE

GOD KNOWS EVERYTHING ABOUT YOU AND HE WANTS YOU TO KNOW EVERYTHING ABOUT HIM!

Draw a picture of yourself under the "you" bubble. Then write something you would like to know more about God. Under the "God" bubble, write a cool memory about something cool that happened to you.

GOD:
I KNOW EVERYTHING ABOUT YOU.
REMEMBER THE TIME WHEN WE...

YOU:
SOMETHING I WANT TO
LEARN ABOUT GOD IS...

ACTIVITY SHEET

God wants to be your closest friend! He knows everything about you, and wants you to know everything about Him.

The verses below talk about knowing God. Write the word KNOW in the blank spaces.

Psalm 9:10 – "*Those who _____ your name trust in you for you, O lord, do not abandon those who search for you.*"

Psalm 119:168 – "*Yes, I obey your commandments and laws because you _____ everything I do.*"

Psalm 139:23 – "*Search me, O God, and _____ my heart.*"

Daniel 11:32 – "*But the people who _____ their God will be strong and will resist him.*"

John 10:27 – "*My sheep listen to my voice; I _____ them, and they follow me.*"

Phil 3:8 – "*Yes, everything else is worthless when compared with the infinite value of _____ing Christ Jesus my Lord. For his sake, I have discarded everything else, counting it all as garbage, so that I could gain Christ and become one with him.*"

Philippians 3:10 – "*I want to _____ Christ and experience the mighty power that raised him from the dead.*"

Colossians 1:10 – "*You will grow as you learn to _____ God better and better.*"

BAZOOKA BREAKDOWN

In one word, describe what is unique about you. Write it here.

What are three ways you get to know God better?

Name one cool thing about God.

Write this verse out three times and see if you can memorize it!
"The Lord is close to all who call on Him." –Psalm 145:18

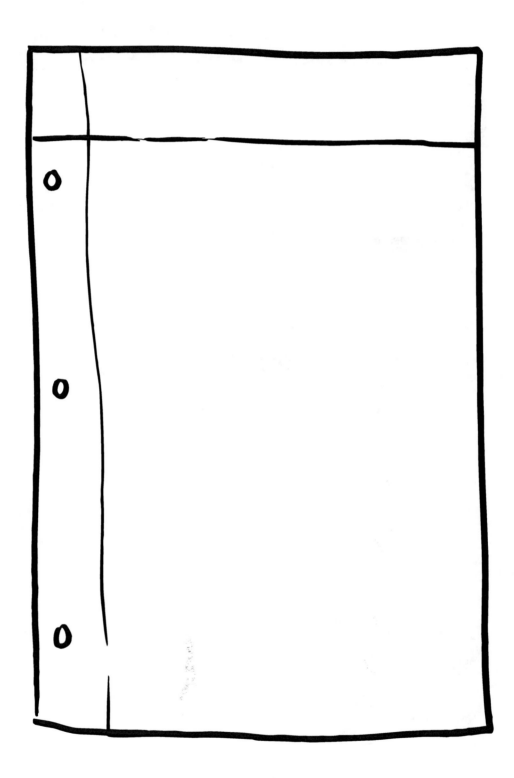

OPTION 1: ROCK NECKLACE

Supplies

- Small rock for each boy
- 22 Gauge colored wire (15 inches for each boy)
- Leather cord (enough to make a necklace for each boy)
- Needle-nose pliers
- Scissors

Directions

- Place a rock at the center of a 15-inch-long piece of colored wire.
- Wrap the wire around the rock a few times to secure it and twist the ends together.
- Wrap the twist around a pencil to make a loop.
- Use needle-nose pliers to close the loop, then cut off any excess wire.
- Hang the pendant from a length of leather cord to make a necklace.

OPTION 2: PET "GOD" ROCKS

Supplies

- Rocks
- Sharpie markers
- Paint (optional)
- Google eyes (optional)
- Glue or glue dots (optional)

Directions

1. Decorate the rocks

2. Write one of the Scripture references on the back of the rock:

- Psalm 25:10
- 1 Peter 1:2
- Psalm 119:11
- Jeremiah 33:3
- Psalm 27:8
- Exodus 4:12
- Psalm 145:18

WHOOSH!

GOD THE FATHER

WHAT'S THE POINT?
GOD IS OUR PERFECT HEAVENLY FATHER.
HE LOVES US, PROTECTS US, AND PROVIDES FOR US.

THEME VERSE:

See how much our Father loves us,
for he calls us his children, and that is what we are!
1 John 3:1

RELATED BIBLE PASSAGE:

Exodus 16:1–31

In the last lesson we talked about the fact that God knows everything about you and wants you to know everything about Him. We talked about how we can learn more about God.

Today we're going to talk some more about what God is like.

There's something about God that is crazy awesome. In fact, it's kind of mind blowing. When you try to think about it, it sometimes makes your brain hurt.

There are three different parts to who God is, yet He is one God. Let me show you what I mean.

I want you to think about three things: water, ice, and steam. What do all three things have in common? They're all made of the same thing - water!

Water can be in liquid form – like when it comes out of the faucet in your kitchen or the hose in your back yard. You can drink it on a hot day. You can take a shower or bath and get cleaned up. You can put it on your flowers and it will help them grow.

But if you took water in liquid form and put it in your freezer for a few hours… something cool would happen to it. It would turn into ice! It's still water – but just different.

And then what if you took some water and put it on the stove and heated it up? It would start boiling and eventually turn into a vapor that would float into the air called steam.

WHAT DO ALL THREE OF THESE THINGS HAVE IN COMMON?

THEY'RE ALL WATER. BUT THEY'RE ALL DIFFERENT FORMS OF THE SAME THING. WATER, ICE, AND STEAM.

God is the same way! There are three parts to Him. They're all different forms, but they are all the same thing. The same way we have water, ice, steam, we have God the Father, God the Son or Jesus, and God the Holy Spirit. They are one, but different. We call this the Trinity—one God in three different parts.

Is your brain hurting?

Over the next few chapters, we're going to talk about the three different parts of God—the Father, Son, and Holy Spirit. We're going to learn about each one of them and what makes them different.

Today we're going to start by talking about God the Father.

I think it's really, really cool that God calls himself "Our Father" because fathers are awesome.

Jarred loves to spend time with his Dad. They have a lot in common, especially when it comes to the outdoors. They both love to be outside, go camping, and ride their bikes. Every year, they go to a special camping spot, just the two of them. They set up their tents, build their campfires, and spend a whole week hiking, fishing, and spending time together.

Jarred loves being with his dad. He always knows his dad will make sure he is safe. Even though they go on some crazy adventures, Jarred doesn't worry because his dad is there with him. Even times when Jarred is nervous, he knows his dad is there to keep him safe.

God the Father is the same way with you and me.

1. GOD IS OUR PROTECTOR

He is always watching over us, protecting us, and keeping us safe from danger and harm. Psalm 121:7–8 explains it in a cool way: *"The Lord keeps you from all harm and watches over your life. The Lord keeps watch over you as you come and go, both now and forever."*

God is always watching over you. In those moments when you feel afraid of something, you can be sure that God is right there with you, keeping you safe. You don't have to be scared or ever, ever, ever feel like you're alone. God is watching over you. He is our protector.

What is a protector? Well, it's like a shield in front of us. Imagine someone was throwing snowballs or water balloons at you (FUN!) when suddenly one of your friends jumps in front of you and blocks the things being thrown at you. When they were standing in front of you – no one could hit you with anything! They protected you by being a shield.

God is your shield! He stands before you and around you and keeps you safe. Psalm 27:1 says, *"The Lord is my light and my salvation—so why should I be afraid? The Lord is my fortress, protecting me from danger, so why should I tremble?"* You don't ever have to be afraid because God is just like a shield, standing in front of you, protecting you from anything that gets thrown at you.

Another great thing about Jarred's camping trips is that his dad makes sure they have everything they'll need. He packs the cooler with food and he catches fish to cook over the fire and eat for dinner. He makes sure he has clothes that are warm enough and shoes that will keep his feet dry. He brings the extra warm sleeping bags for the nights when it gets cold. Jarred never has to worry, because he knows his dad will provide everything he needs.

God the Father is the same way with you and me.

 ## 2. GOD IS OUR PROVIDOR

Everything you and I have has been given to us by God the Father. You might think that your parents get you everything you need, but the Bible tells us everything we have comes from God. He provides a job for your mom and dad so they can earn money to buy you things. He makes sure that you have the things you need every single day.

There is a story in Exodus chapter 16 that tells us about God providing for His people. The Israelites were slaves in the nation of Egypt. They had no rights and no freedom. They had to do slave labor all day—whatever the Egyptians told them to do. It was like they were prisoners! One day God used our friend named Moses to lead the Israelites in a huge escape attempt. Even though the Egyptians chased them, God did some cool miracles and all of the Israelites escaped from Egypt. They were free! But now they were in the desert, looking for a new place to live and unfortunately, there was nothing to eat! They were so hungry and wondered what they were going to do.

So they prayed to God and He did something amazing. In the morning, when they got out of their tents and went outside, there was food called "manna" covering the ground. Every morning, they would wake up, look outside, and see food on the ground. God provided food for them every single day!

God is your provider. He provides your food, your clothes, and your house. Even though He might

not give you every single thing you want, He provides everything you need. Sometimes we can worry about things, but it's important to remember that God will always provide for everything we need.

Matthew 6:25–27 says this: *"That is why I tell you not to worry about everyday life—whether you have enough food and drink, or enough clothes to wear. Isn't life more than food, and your body more that clothing? Look at the birds. They don't plant or harvest or store food in barns, for your Heavenly Father feeds them. And aren't you far more valuable to Him than they are? Can all your worries add a single moment to your life?"*

Did you catch that? You know all those birds you can see flying around your house during summer time? The Bible says that God looks after them and makes sure they have a place to live and food to eat. And God cares about you way more than the birds, so of course He is going to make sure you are taken care of. He is our Heavenly Father.

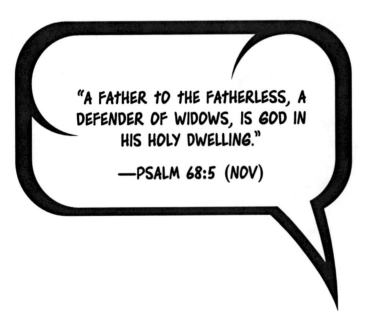

"A FATHER TO THE FATHERLESS, A DEFENDER OF WIDOWS, IS GOD IN HIS HOLY DWELLING."

—PSALM 68:5 (NOV)

Sometimes our earthly fathers mess up and make mistakes. Sometimes they say things that hurt. Sometimes they have to work and can't be there when we really need them. Some boys grow up not knowing their earthly father because he left a long time ago.

Sometimes dads make mistakes, but not God.

You know what makes God, our Heavenly Father, so awesome?

 # 3. GOD THE FATHER IS PERFECT

God the Father never makes mistakes. He always does the right thing. He always does what's best for you and He will never, ever leave you.

No matter how much your mom and dad love you, they are still people just like you and me. And people make mistakes. How many of you here have ever made a mistake? How many of you have ever said or done something mean? How many of you have ever done something you wish you could take back? All of us have, because we are humans, and humans are not perfect.

But God is not human. He is God. He never makes mistakes. That makes me feel so safe! I can know that no matter what, God will do the right thing for me every time. I don't ever have to wonder if God forgot about me or if He doesn't love me anymore. He will never let me down. He will never fail me. He will never do anything that isn't perfect.

Just so you know: Some boys don't have a dad in their life. There are lots of reasons this may be the case. You should know that it is never your fault if you don't have a dad who is close to you. It must be really hard sometimes to wish you had a dad like other boys, but you should know that God promises He will be the very best Father you could ever imagine. There's even a verse in the Bible just for you. Psalm 68:5 says, *"A father to the fatherless, a defender of widows, is God in His holy dwelling."* (NIV) You may not have a father here on earth, or maybe you do have a father but you're not close to him. God will step in and be the best father you ever dreamed of having. It's His promise to you.

God is your Heavenly Father. He loves you so much. It's like you're His favorite, and He is so proud of you. Whenever you're scared, imagine your Heavenly Father standing like a shield in front of you. When you're worried about something, remember that He is your Father who will give you everything you need. And when you need someone to be there for you, you can count always count on God, your Heavenly Father.

Closing Prayer: God, thank you for being my Father. It makes me feel strong and safe knowing You are there with me. Help me to always remember that I am your son, that you love me and are proud of me. Amen.

DOODLE PAGE

LESSON 2

Draw as MANY things as you can that God
has provided for you and your family!

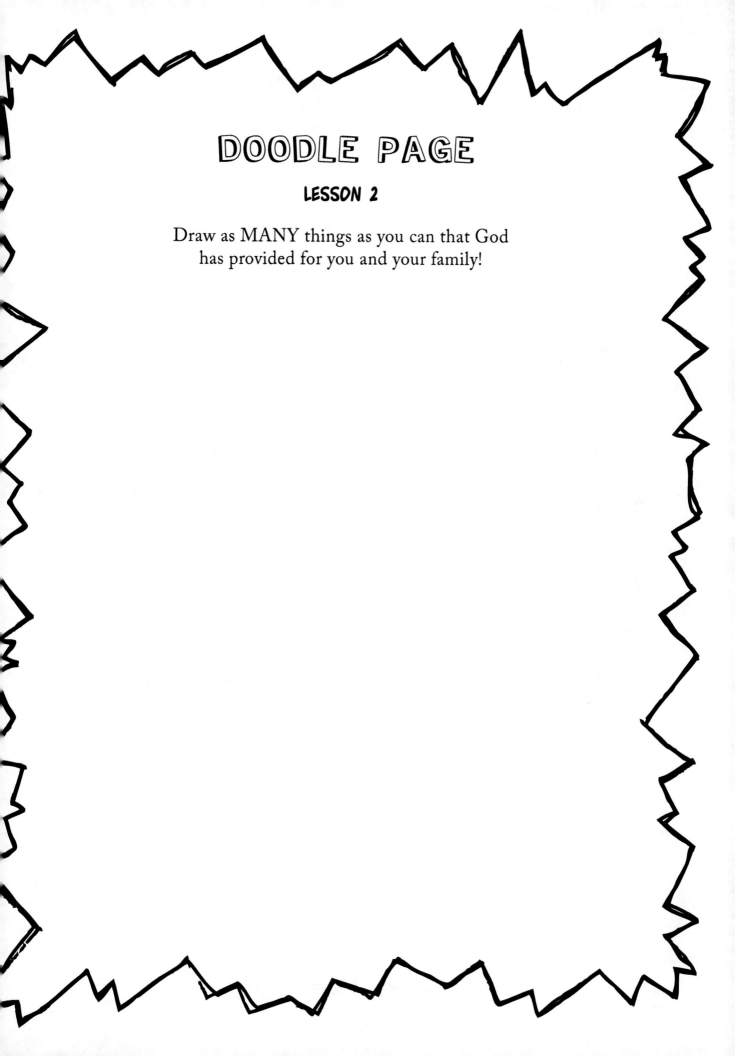

God is the Best Father EVER! Write words that describe God the Father that begin with each letter provided below.

F _____

A _____

T _____

H _____

E _____

R _____

WORD LIST

Fun	Truth	Everywhere
Awesome	Holy	Ready to Listen

In the verses below, write in the word FATHER in the blank spaces.

Psalm 2:7 – "*The Lord said to me, 'You are my son. Today I have become your* _____ '"

Psalm 89:26 – *"And he will call out to me, "You are my* _____, *my God, and the Rock of my salvation."'*

Isaiah 9:6 – "*And He will be called: Wonderful Counselor, Mighty God, Everlasting* _____, *Prince of Peace."*

Matthew 5:16 – *"In the same way, let your good deeds shine out for all to see, so that everyone will praise your heavenly* _____."

Romans 8:15 – "*So you have not received a spirit that makes you fearful slaves. Instead, you received God's Spirit when he adopted you as his own children. Now we call him, 'Abba* _____.' *For His spirit joins with our spirit to affirm that we are God's children."*

2 Cor 6:18 – *"And I will be your* _____, *and you will be my sons and daughters, says the Lord Almighty."*

BAZOOKA BREAKDOWN

If someone was in danger – how would you protect them? Draw a picture showing what you would do!

Name three things God provides for your family?

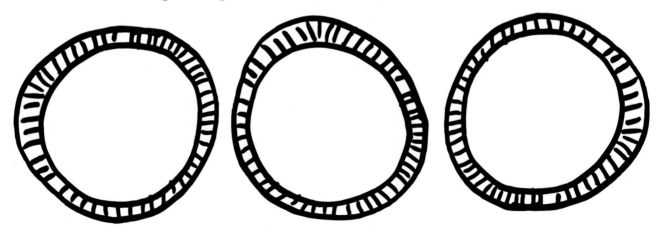

Bazooka Boys ★ Knowing God

Do you know anyone who is perfect?

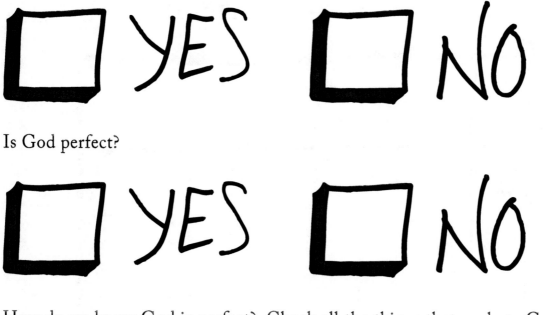

☐ YES   ☐ NO

Is God perfect?

☐ YES   ☐ NO

How do we know God is perfect? Check all the things that apply to God.

☐ **HE NEVER MAKES MISTAKES.**

☐ **HE PROTECTS US.**

☐ **HE PROVIDES FOR US.**

☐ **HE LOVES US.**

Write out this verse three times and see if you can memorize it!

"See how much our Father loves us, for he calls us his children, and that is what we are!" –1 John 3:1

BIBLE SHIELDS

Supplies

- Cardboard
- Scissors
- Crayons/markers
- Duct Tape
- Bible verses
- Rolled up paper for balls (ping pong balls work great too)

Directions

- Cut the cardboard into enough shield.
- Use the Duct Tape to create a handle on the back of the shield.
- Design the front of a shield with markers and Duct Tape.
- Write the reference of one of the Bible verses, listed in Bazooka Blitz, on the front of your shield.

Bazooka Boys ★ Knowing God

WEEK 3

GOD THE SON (JESUS)

What's the Point?
Jesus came to earth and died on the cross
to give us an all access pass to God.

THEME VERSE:

So now we can rejoice in our wonderful new relationship with God because our Lord Jesus Christ has made us friends of God.

Romans 5:11

RELATED BIBLE PASSAGE:

Genesis 3

Jesus is God's Son. He was in heaven with the Father and the Holy Spirit, but there was a problem with people on the earth that God had created. How many of you have heard the story of Adam and Eve?

Adam and Eve were the first people God ever created. Genesis 1 tells us about God creating man and woman and giving them one rule. They were not supposed to eat the fruit from a certain tree in the garden. But Adam and Eve did not follow the rules that God gave them, and the moment that they disobeyed God, sin entered the world. Sin is not just the things you and I do that are wrong—sin became part of who we are.

Do you have little brothers or sisters? Have heard them say "Mine!" and get kind of mean? Have you had them hit you or be selfish? Who taught them to be naughty? Did you teach your little sister to be mean? Did your mom and dad sit them down and tell them that they should scream and cry when they don't get their own way? No! They were just born that way. You and I were too.

Each and every one of us was born with a sinful nature. The Bible tells us in Romans 3:23: *"For everyone has sinned; we all fall short of God's glorious standard."* Every one of us makes mistakes, does the wrong thing, and thinks only about ourselves. It doesn't mean that we're bad, it just means that we're born imperfect. We're born with a sinful nature.

But God is perfect. He doesn't have a sinful nature like you and me. He never does the wrong thing. He has never sinned. He is perfect. And because He is perfect and holy, He cannot be around sin. He just can't.

God loves us so much that He wanted to find a way to be close to us even though our nature is sinful. This is where Jesus comes in. John 3:16 says, *"For*

God loved the world so much that He gave His one and only son, so that everyone who believes in Him will not perish but have eternal life."

Jesus is God's son. He is perfect and sinless just like God the Father. So God came up with a plan. Jesus would come down to earth as a person just like you and me. He would be fully God and yet fully human. And He would live a perfect life without sinning at all. Who knows how Jesus came to earth? What holiday celebrates when Jesus came down to earth? That's right—Christmas! Jesus came down to earth as a little baby who was born in a stable and laid in a manger on Christmas!

"FOR GOD LOVED THE WORLD SO MUCH THAT HE GAVE HIS ONE AND ONLY SON, SO THAT EVERYONE WHO BELIEVES IN HIM WILL NOT PERISH BUT HAVE ETERNAL LIFE."
—JOHN 3:16

Jesus came to earth for a very important reason. The only way God could be close to us was if Jesus died on the cross and rose again. If He did that, there would be a way for us to have a close relationship with God even though we're sinful people. So that's exactly what Jesus did.

Jesus came to earth, grew up and became a man, and lived a sinless life. When He was 33 years old, He died on the cross. But three days after He died, He rose again! And then He went back up to heaven to be with the Father once again.

When He did that, something amazing happened—now we have a way to be close to God. Even

33

though we're sinful people, you and I can have a relationship with God because of what Jesus did on the cross! Isn't that awesome?

There was a boy named Cameron who went to see his favorite football team play a championship game. Not only was this his favorite team, but his favorite quarterback in the whole world was playing in this game. He couldn't believe he was going to get to see him play in person!

After the game was over, he noticed people walking through a door that said "Locker Room Access." He wondered what was back there and so he walked closer to get a better look. On the other side of the door, he saw the quarterback— his favorite quarterback— standing outside the locker room! Cameron could hardly believe what he was seeing. He saw other people walking through the door, so he walked over, crazy excited that he was going to get the chance to meet his favorite player.

But the security guard at the door stopped him and said, "I'm sorry, but you can't go back there without one of these." He held up a lanyard that had a little

card on the bottom that said "All Access." He was so disappointed. He knew that his absolute favorite, favorite, favorite football player was right behind that door and if he could just get through, he would be able to meet him and get to know him and spend time with him. But he couldn't get through that door without the all access pass.

Then all of the sudden, a coach walked up beside him and smiled. He held up something in his hand. Cameron could hardly believe it—it was an all access pass. The nice man looked at him and said, "Would you like to have this?"

Would he like to have this pass? Are you kidding me? Of course he wanted the pass! Like crazy! With that pass he could spend time with the most amazingly awesome person in the universe!

He could hardly get the words out of his mouth. "Yes! I would love it! Thank you so much!" The coach placed the lanyard around his neck and Cameron walked through the door and got to meet his favorite football player.

That's exactly what Jesus did for you and me. We were separated from God. We couldn't be close to Him because of our sinful nature. There was a big door between us and Him. But when Jesus came to earth and died on the cross, He

> SO NOW WE CAN REJOICE IN OUR WONDERFUL NEW RELATIONSHIP WITH GOD BECAUSE OUR LORD JESUS CHRIST HAS MADE US FRIENDS OF GOD.
> —ROMANS 5:11

made a way for you and me to have an all access pass to God. We can have a relationship with Him. We can know Him. We can be close to Him. Through Jesus, we can be forgiven of all our sins!

So how do you get that all access pass to God? Simply ask Jesus for it! Ask Him to come into your life and forgive you for all the things you've done wrong. Ask Him to come and live in your heart. When you ask Jesus into your life, He places a big all access pass around your neck. You're forgiven of your sins and can have a close, personal relationship with God. Romans 5:11 says, *"So now we can rejoice in our wonderful new relationship with God because our Lord Jesus Christ has made us friends of God."*

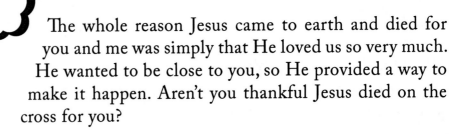

The whole reason Jesus came to earth and died for you and me was simply that He loved us so very much. He wanted to be close to you, so He provided a way to make it happen. Aren't you thankful Jesus died on the cross for you?

Maybe some of you have never asked Jesus to come into your hearts and you want to ask Him to forgive you of your sins and put a big all access pass around your neck. Today you can invite Jesus into your life and begin living your life in a close, personal relationship with Him.

Jesus would love to have a relationship with you. He died on the cross because He loved you so much and today you can ask Him to come into your heart. If you would like to do that, all you have to do is pray this prayer and begin living your life for Him.

Closing Prayer: "Dear Jesus, thank You for coming to earth and dying on the cross. Please forgive me for all my sins and come into my life. I want to live for You, and I want to spend time getting to know You more so I can be closer to You. Thank You for coming into my heart. Amen."

DOODLE PAGE

LESSON 3

"When Jesus came to earth and died on the cross, He made a way for us to be close to God. Draw a bridge that symbolized what Jesus did for us.

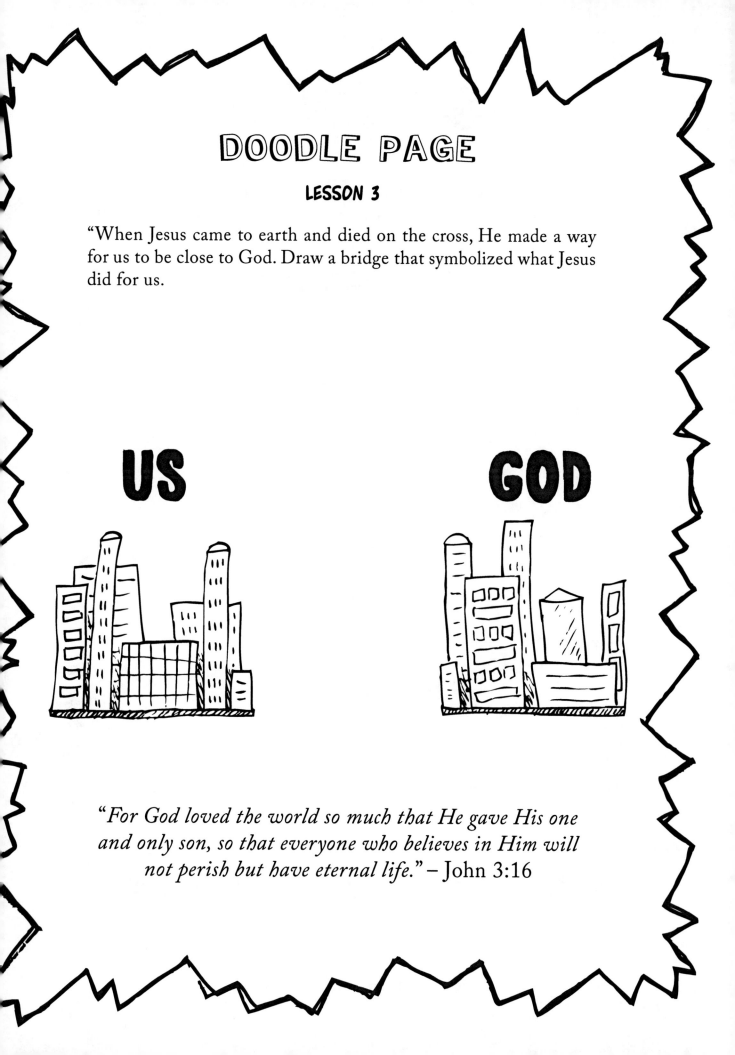

US

GOD

"For God loved the world so much that He gave His one and only son, so that everyone who believes in Him will not perish but have eternal life." – John 3:16

ACTIVITY SHEET

Romans 5:8 says, "But God showed his great love for us by sending Christ to die for us while we were still sinners." Draw a picture describing this verse.

Romans 5 talks about how sin entered the world through the sin of Adam, and how Jesus coming provided a way for us to be forgiven of our sins. Read through Romans 5 in your Bible, and write out the following verses below.

Romans 5:12: _____

_____

_____.

Romans 5:15 _____

_____

_____.

Romans 5:16 _____

_____

_____.

Romans 5:17 _____

_____

_____.

Romans 5:18 _____

_____

_____.

Now write out a prayer thanking God for His salvation and what He did for us on the cross:

_____

_____

_____

_____

_____

_____

_____

_____

_____

_____

_____

_____

_____.

BAZOOKA BREAKDOWN

If you could have an all access pass to meet anyone, who would it be?" Write his/her name her and then cut out some pictures of them and glue them in the space provided.

MY HERO

How can we get an all access pass to God?"

BY BELIEVING IN

_ _ _ _ _ _

AND GIVING OUR

LIVES TO HIM.

ALL ACCESS PASS

3. Why did God send His only son, Jesus, to die for us?"

Write this verse out three times and see if you can memorize it!

"So now we can rejoice in our wonderful new relationship with God because our Lord Jesus Christ has made us friends of God." –Romans 5:11

DUCT TAPE ALL ACCESS LANYARD

<u>Supplies</u>

- Duct tape (three feet)
- Scissors
- Key rings
- Sharpie markers
- Laynard hooks (optional)
- Cardstock (optional)
- Single hole punch

<u>Directions</u>

1. Measure three feet of duct tape

2. Fold the duct tape in half the long way, sticky sides together. (Hint: Do it slowly—once the two sticky sides touch, there's no pulling them apart. It might be easier to work with three 12" pieces, overlapping the ends.

3. Make a loop by putting the two ends through your key ring (you can put it around your neck if that would be easier).

4. Fold the pieces over the key ring and tape them to the straps (2" x 1" strip of tape).

5. If needed, secure the straps with another piece of tape.

6. Write "All Access Pass" down the length of the duct tape

7. Optional:
   - Attach a lanyard hook to the key ring
   - Cut a 3" x 4" piece of cardstock
   - Cover both sides of the cardstock with duct tape and trim off excess tape
   - Punch a hole in the middle of the top of the cardstock
   - Attach the cardstock to the lanyard hook
   - Write "All Access Pass" on the cardstock

GOD THE HOLY SPIRIT

WHAT'S THE POINT?

JESUS SENT US THE HOLY SPIRIT TO GIVE US POWER
AND BE OUR TEACHER AND GUIDE.

THEME VERSE

*Then I will ask the Father to send you the Holy Spirit
who will help you and always be with you.*

John 14:16 (CEV)

RELATED BIBLE STORY

Acts 2:1–4

Have you have ever played tag? You chase everyone around the room, and when you finally touch someone, what do you say? "Tag—you're it!"

In the last chapter, we talked about Jesus coming to earth and dying on the cross to make a way for us have an all access pass to God. When Jesus lived on earth, He picked twelve people called the disciples to be His friends and travel around with Him while He taught them all the things they needed to know about God.

But after Jesus rose from the dead, He told the disciples He was going to leave. He was going back to heaven. John 16:5 says, "But now I am going away to the one who sent me." Can you imagine how the disciples must have felt?

Have you ever had a really good friend move away? Someone you loved hanging out with and spending time together? When they told you they were leaving, how did you feel? You probably felt bummed and disappointed and sad and lots of other things.

The disciples felt the same way when Jesus told them He was leaving earth and going back to heaven, but then Jesus told them something else really amazing. He said that He had to go away, but He was going to send someone back to earth to be here with us forever. Do you know who that is? The Holy Spirit. Jesus had to leave, but when He left He said "Tag—you're it!" to the Holy Spirit! Now it's the Holy Spirit's job to teach us and speak to us and show us all the things we need to know.

John 15:26 says, *"I will send you the Spirit who comes from the Father and shows what is true. The Spirit will help you and will tell you about me"* (CEV).

So Jesus went back up into heaven and a few days later, the Holy Sprit came down to the disciples. Now, instead of Jesus teaching them all the things about God and helping them know what to do, the Holy Spirit would speak to them and guide them. And He is still here and will speak to you and me to help us know God better!

The big difference is that the Holy Spirit doesn't have a human body like Jesus did. You can't see Him. You can't hear His voice with your ears like you can hear your teachers at school telling you things, but you can hear Him speak in your heart. Sometimes you will just have a gut feeling, and that's the Holy Spirit speaking to you. We can't see Him with our eyes, but He is always with us.

The Bible talks about a few specific things the Holy Spirit does.

First, the Holy Spirit . . .

 1. MAKES US STRONG

Who is the most powerful person you can think of? Superman? A professional wrestler? A football player? Being powerful means you're not only strong, but you know how to use your strength in the best way possible.

Acts 1:8 says, *"But you will receive power when the Holy Spirit comes upon you."* When the Holy Spirit comes and lives in our lives, it gives us the power to stand up for what's right. It gives us the courage to tell others about Jesus. It makes us strong and able to do great things for God.

I don't know about you, but I want to be as strong as I can possibly be! Sometimes I don't feel very strong. Sometimes I'm afraid or feel nervous about things. But you know what? Whenever you're scared or nervous or sad, the Holy Spirit will help you. He is with you wherever you go—all the time! Say a prayer and ask Him to help you feel brave and strong, and He will help you get through whatever it is you're facing.

The second thing the Holy Spirit does is promise to. . .

 ## 2. BE YOUR TEACHER

Jackson loves his teacher, Mr. Crenshaw. He's the best teacher ever and shows Jackson how to do all kinds of really cool things and helps him understand stuff that is hard to understand. He's patient and always willing to listen whenever Jackson has a question. He's really encouraging and always tells Jackson he's doing a good job.

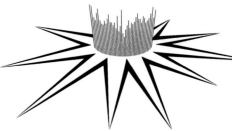

But Mr. Crenshaw helps Jackson in another way. Whenever Jackson has a spelling test, he hands it in to Mr. Crenshaw, who takes out a big red marker and circles all the words he got wrong.

When Jackson sees the big red marks, he knows what he needs to work on and the things he needs to try harder at.

The Holy Spirit is a great teacher, too. He'll show you all kinds of things about God. He'll help you understand the Bible. He'll help you know what Jesus wants you to do and show you how to live a life that makes God the Father happy. John 14:26 says, *"The Companion, the Holy Spirit, whom the Father will send in my name, will teach you everything and will remind you of everything I told you."* (CEB)

"THE COMPANION, THE HOLY SPIRIT, WHOM THE FATHER WILL SEND IN MY NAME, WILL TEACH YOU EVERYTHING AND WILL REMIND YOU OF EVERYTHING I TOLD YOU."

—JOHN 14:26 (CEB)

The Holy Spirit will also help you know when you've done something wrong. How many of you have ever made a mistake or done something wrong and all of the sudden you get a feeling in your gut that makes you feel really bad about what you did? That's the Holy Spirit! He'll draw big red circles around the things in your life that you need to change and areas of your behavior or attitude that don't make God happy. He shows us these things so we can learn to do better and make the right choices.

The last thing the Holy Spirit does is . . .

 3. GUIDE YOU

Have you ever been lost? Have you ever looked around and realized you didn't know which way to go? Sometimes it's easy for us to get lost in our lives. We don't know what we should do, but the Holy Spirit promises to guide us!

Joshua had a big decision to make. He had been asked to join the traveling baseball team for the summer, but if he joined the team, he knew he would miss out on a lot of other activities he wanted to be part of. He couldn't decide what to do! His mom and dad told him he needed to make his own decision, but Joshua was torn. Although he loved playing baseball, he was also interested in going to summer camp and taking drum lessons and even spending some extra time with his little brother. He needed help to know what to do.

So Joshua prayed. He asked God to help him make the decision. One morning he woke up, and in his gut, he knew what his decision should be. It was so crazy! Nothing in particular happened, he just knew that he should pass o n baseball this year and spend time doing other things.
It just felt like the right thing.

What changed? How did Joshua know what to do? The Holy Spirit guided him in making the right decision. When he prayed, he was asking for the Holy Spirit's help, and He gave Joshua the answer he was looking for.

If you don't know what to do in a situation, why not stop and ask the Holy Spirit to guide you? Maybe you're not sure if you should say something. Ask the Holy Spirit if you should speak up or stay quiet. Maybe you're wondering if you should do something your friends are doing. The Holy Spirit will speak to you and help you know what the right thing is, and He'll give you the courage to do the right thing too!

Psalm 143:10 says, *"Teach me to do your will, for you are my God. May your gracious Spirit lead me forward on a firm footing."* God will guide you. The Holy Spirit will speak to you and help you know where to go, what to say, and how to act.

Aren't you glad that Jesus sent us the Holy Spirit? I'm so thankful that when Jesus left, He didn't leave us all on earth alone with no one to show what to do. I'm glad he "tagged" the Holy Spirit to come down to earth to make us strong, be our teacher, and guide us.

Closing Prayer: Dear God, Thank You for sending the Holy Spirit to help me. Thank you that I can know He will make me stronger, teach me things about You, and guide me into making the right choices in my life. Help me to know His voice. Amen.

DOODLE PAGE

LESSON 4

The Holy Spirit teaches us, guides us, and makes us stronger. In the space provided, write one thing that the Holy Spirit is teaching you, one way the Holy Spirit is guiding you, and how the Holy Spirit is making you stronger.

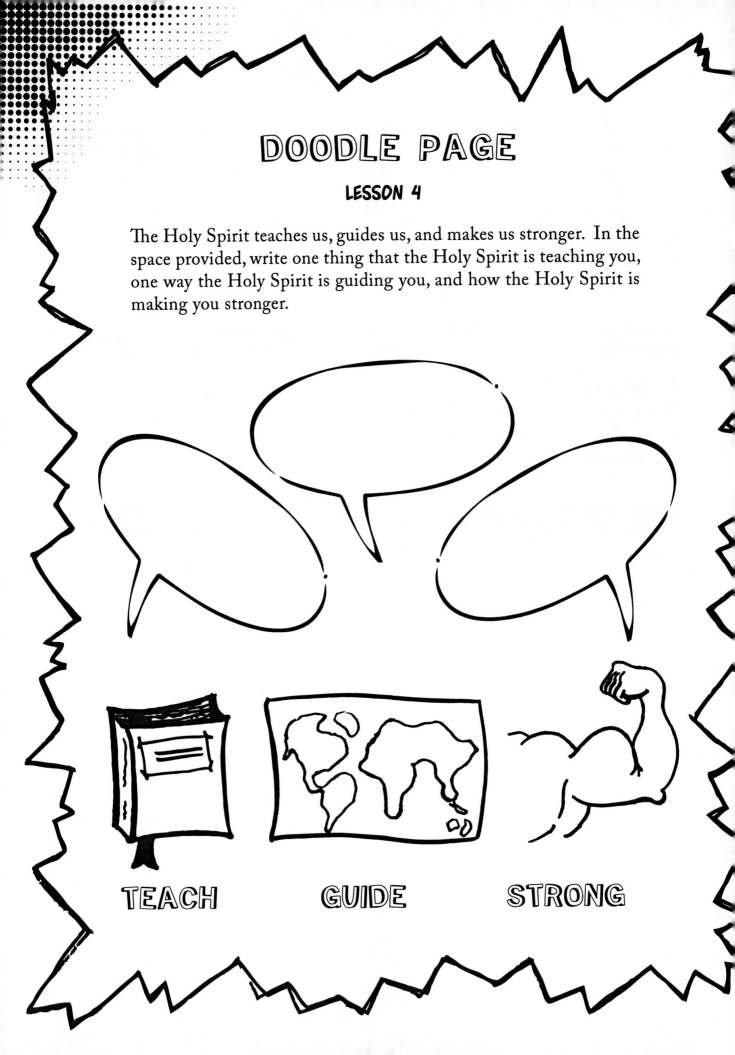

TEACH   **GUIDE**   **STRONG**

ACTIVITY SHEET

WEEK 4

Solve the puzzle by substituting the numbers for the letters.

1	2	3	4	5	6	7	8	9	10	11	12	13	14	15
A	Q	I	P	F	V	X	N	Y	D	W	Z	K	S	G

16	17	18	19	20	21	22	23	24	25	26
O	U	R	C	E	M	H	T	L	J	B

___   ___ ___ ___ ___   ___ ___ ___   ___ ___ ___
3   11 3 24 24   1 14 13   23 22 20

___ ___ ___ ___ ___ ___.   ___ ___ ___   ___ ___
5 1 23 22 20 18   1 8 10   22 20

___ ___ ___ ___   ___ ___ ___ ___   ___ ___ ___
11 3 24 24   15 3 6 20   9 16 17

___ ___ ___ ___ ___ ___ ___   ___ ___ ___ ___ ___ ___
1 8 16 23 22 20 18   5 18 3 20 8 10

___ ___   ___ ___ ___ ___   ___ ___ ___   ___ ___ ___
23 16   22 20 24 4   9 16 17   1 8 10

___ ___   ___ ___   ___ ___ ___ ___   ___ ___ ___
23 16   26 20   11 3 23 22   9 16 17

14:16 NIV

___ ___ ___ ___ ___ ___ ___.   ___ ___ ___ ___
5 16 18 20 6 20 18   25 16 22 8

53

Look up each scripture in the Bible and fill in the blank (the words are listed below).

But you will receive _____ when the Holy Spirit comes on you; and you will be my witnesses in Jerusalem, and in Judea and Samaria, and to the ends of the earth. – Acts 1:8 (NIV)

³Give _____ to the God and Father of our Lord Jesus Christ! He is the Father who gives tender love. All comfort comes from him. ⁴He _____ us in all our troubles. Now we can comfort others when they are in trouble. We ourselves have received comfort from God. – 2 Corinthians 1:3-4 (CEV)

I will send the _____ to you from the Father. He is the Spirit of truth, who comes out from the Father. When the Friend comes to _____ you, he will give witness about me. – John 15:26 (CEV)

I baptize you with water, but he will baptize you with the _____. – Mark 1:8 (NIV)

The angel answered, 'The Holy Spirit will come on you, and the _____ of the Most High will overshadow you. So the holy one to be born will be called the Son of God'. – Luke 1:35 (NIV)

May the God of hope fill you with all _____ and _____ as you trust in him, so that you may overflow with hope by the power of the Holy Spirit. – Romans 15:13 (NIV)

But the _____ of the Spirit is love, joy, peace, forbearance, kindness, goodness, faithfulness, gentleness and self-control. Against such things there is no law. – Galatians 5:22, 23 (NIV)

You _____ me with your counsel. – Psalm 73:24 (NIV)

But the _____ , the Holy Spirit, whom the Father will send in my name, will _____ you all things and will remind you of everything I have said to you. – John 14:26 (NIV)

¹⁰ Just as Jesus was coming up out of the _____ , he saw heaven being torn open and the _____ descending on him like a dove. ¹¹ And a voice came from heaven: "You are my _____ , whom I love; with you I am well pleased. – Mark 1:10, 11 (NIV)

BAZOOKA BREAKDOWN

The Holy Spirit makes us strong. Name one area of your life where you want to be stronger.

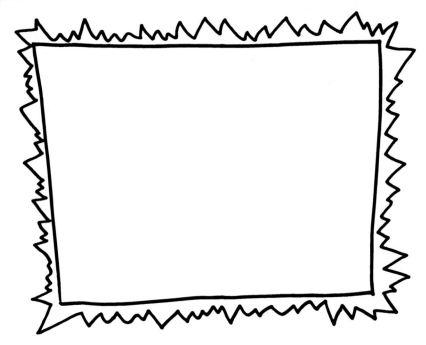

The list below shows some of the ways the Holy Spirit teaches us. Put a check mark next to the things that the Holy Spirit has taught you!

☐ HE WILL TEACH YOU ABOUT JESUS

☐ HE WILL HELP YOU UNDERSTAND THE BIBLE

☐ HE WILL HELP YOU KNOW WHEN YOU'VE DONE SOMETHING WRONG.

☐ HE WILL REMIND YOU OF THINGS YOU HAVE LEARNED.

☐ HE WILL TELL YOU TO HELP OTHER PEOPLE.

☐ HE WILL GIVE YOU COURAGE TO TELL OTHERS ABOUT JESUS.

The Holy Spirit will also be our guide. Is there something the Holy Spirit it asking you to do right now? Take a minute and ask Him to show you something He would like you to do. Listen carefully and then write out what He speaks to your heart in the space provided.

Write out this verse three times and then try to memorize it!

"Then I will ask the Father to send you the Holy Spirit who will help you and always be with you." –John 14:16 (CEV)

MAGNETIC COMPASS PROJECT

<u>Supplies:</u>

- Bowl of water
- Sewing pin or needle
- Magnet
- Small piece of craft foam, cork or paper.

<u>Directions:</u>

1. Cut a small circle from the craft foam, cork or paper.

2. Turn the sewing needle into a magnet by stroking the needle across the magnet about thirty to forty times. Be sure to stroke in one direction only. Not back and forth. The needle will then be magnetized.

3. Place the needle on to the circle cut from your chosen material.

4. Place the circle in the middle of a bowl of water away from the edge of the bowl.

5. The needle will begin to slowly turn around and eventually it will point North and South.

6. Check the accuracy with an actual compass or compass app.

Every magnet has a north and south pole. A compass is a small magnet that aligns itself with the north and south poles of the Earth's magnetic field. As the needle is stroked across the magnet, it becomes magnetized because the electrons within the needle straighten up and align themselves with the magnet. The magnetized needle then aligns itself with the Earth's magnetic field when it is placed on top of the water. If you don't know what to do in a situation, why not stop and ask the Holy Spirit to guide you?

CPSIA information can be obtained
at www.ICGtesting.com
Printed in the USA
FFOW02n1628190217
32533FF

9 780984 031283